Contents

Icons used in this book

This 'pointer' icon marks the brief introduction that sets the piece of writing in context and provides useful background information.

This 'be safe' icon marks important information relating to the use of the text – including personal safety.

This icon indicates that it would be useful for you to have access to a dictionary.

The Green Cross Code

The first version of the Green Cross Code was produced in the 1970s. The Code is still used today. Its aim is to help all children to keep safe when crossing the road.

1 First find a safe place to cross

- If possible, cross the road using: islands, zebra, puffin, pelican or toucan crossings, subways, footbridges, or where there is a crossing point controlled by a police officer, a school crossing patrol or a traffic warden.
- Otherwise, choose a place where you can see clearly in all directions, and where drivers can see you.
- Try to avoid crossing between parked cars, on sharp bends or close to the top of a hill. Move to a space where drivers and riders can see you clearly.
- There should be space to reach the pavement on the other side.

2 Stop just before you get to the kerb

- Do not get too close to the traffic. If there is no pavement, keep back from the edge of the road but make sure you can still see approaching traffic.
- Give yourself lots of time to have a good look all around.

3 Look all around for traffic and listen

- Look in every direction.
- Listen carefully because you can sometimes hear traffic before you can see it.

4 If traffic is coming, let it pass

- Look all around again and listen.
- Do not cross until there is a safe gap in the traffic and you are certain that there is plenty of time.
- Remember, even if traffic is a long way off, it may be approaching very quickly.

5 When it is safe, go straight across the road – do not run

- Keep looking and listening for traffic while you cross, in case there is any traffic you did not see, or in case other traffic appears suddenly.
- Look out for cyclists and motorcyclists travelling between lanes of traffic.
- When it is safe, go straight across the road. Do not cross diagonally.

Department for Transport

1. Which of your senses are involved in crossing roads safely, according to this code? (ring those that the code mentions)

sight touch sound smell taste

2 marks

2. Which words tell you that it is as important to **be seen** as to **see**?

____

1 mark

3. Why is it wise to cross a road in a straight line rather than diagonally?

____

____

1 mark

4. Name **three** places where you should avoid crossing the road.

____

____

____

3 marks

5. Name **three** places where it is good to cross.

____

____

____

3 marks

6. Where should you stand when getting ready to cross the road?

____

1 mark

7. Why is it unsafe to cross the road on a sharp bend or just below the top of a hill?

____

____

1 mark

page 5
total out of 12

Games glossary

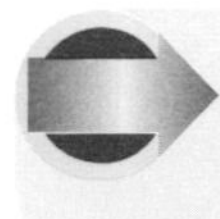

This text explains some key words to do with ball games like rounders, tennis and basketball. Some of the words may be new to you, so read carefully.

backboard board which holds the shooting ring for basketball

backhand stroke tennis shot played with the back of the racket

backstop fielder who stands behind the batter in rounders

bat hitting the ball in rounders

bounce pass pass where the ball hits the ground first

bowl throwing the ball to the batter

chest pass throwing the ball from chest high in a game of basketball

cool-down exercises to relax your body after a game

dribble/dribbling bouncing the ball and running in basketball

field catching and throwing the ball in rounders

forehand stroke tennis shot played with the front of the racket

hamstring large group of muscles at top, back, of your legs

hitting T stand for the ball to sit on in rounders

joints parts of your body where two bones join together, like your shoulders, elbows and knees

muscles parts of your body which help you to bend and stretch

overarm pass throwing the ball with your arm up high

ring circle which the ball must go through to score in basketball

rounder making a score in rounders. At the end of a game, the team with the most rounders wins.

serve way of starting a game of short tennis

shooting trying to throw the ball at the backboard so it drops through the ring in basketball

stretching moving your joints and muscles as much as you can

underarm throw throwing a ball up with your arm starting down low

volley hitting a ball before it hits the ground

warm-up way of moving to get your body ready for exercise

From *You Can Do it! Games*
Kirk Bizley

1. A glossary is like a small (ring **one**):

index dictionary introduction summary.

1 mark

2. The glossary is arranged alphabetically. (ring **one**)

True / False

1 mark

3. a) If the word 'penalty' were added to this glossary, where would it fit?

   It would fit after ______________________ and before ______________.

1 mark

   b) The word 'head' would fit after ______________ and before ______________.

1 mark

4. Why does 'backstop' come before 'bat'?

____

____

1 mark

5. Which tennis shot is the opposite of a backhand stroke?

____

1 mark

6. What is the name of the group of muscles at the rear, top of your legs?

____

1 mark

7. In which game might you perform a chest pass?

____

1 mark

8. Find **two** entries that describe ways of exercising rather than playing a sport.

____

____

2 marks

9. In this text, are the words 'bat' and 'field' nouns or verbs? Explain how you know this.

____

____

2 marks

page 7
total out of 12

The baby of the family

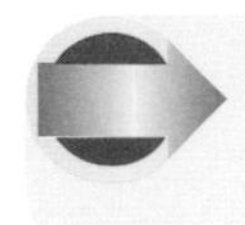

This poem was written by the bestselling British poet Wendy Cope, who has written poems for both adults and children.

Up on Daddy's shoulders
He is riding high –
The baby of the family,
A pleased, pork pie.
I'm tired and my feet are sore –
It seems all wrong.
He's lucky to be little
But it won't last long.

The baby of the family,
He grabs my toys
And when I grab them back he makes
A big, loud noise.
I mustn't hit him, so I chant
This short, sweet song:
"You're lucky to be little
But it won't last long."

Everybody looks at him
And thinks he's sweet,
Even when he bellows "No!"
And stamps his feet.
He won't be so amusing
When he's tall and strong.
It's lovely being little
But it won't last long.

Wendy Cope

1. What relation is the speaker to the baby of the family?

____ 1 mark

2. Which word best describes the strongest feeling of the speaker? (ring **one**)

impatient   tired   jealous   wary   bored   1 mark

3. a) Why do you think the baby was riding on Daddy's shoulders?

____ 1 mark

____

b) What else can the words 'riding high' mean?

____ 1 mark

____

4. Name **one** of the adjectives that the speaker uses to describe his or her song.

____ 1 mark

5. How do you think singing the song makes the speaker feel – and why?

____ 1 mark

____

6. What 'won't last long' and why?

____ 2 marks

____

7. Which **two** words in the poem are used to rhyme with the words 'high' and 'noise'?

____ 2 marks

____

page 9
total out of 10

Invasion

This text is taken from a book called *I'm Telling You They're Aliens* by Jeremy Strong. He has written many funny stories for children.

The trouble is people think you're very strange if you go round saying things about alien invasions, and if you're not very careful they come and take you away and lock you up and feed you on things like rice pudding (which I hate).

So who do you tell? Do you go to the police? Do you tell the kids in your class? They already think I'm half-mad anyway, and they wouldn't listen to me anyhow, not after that episode with the non-existent asteroid.

I decided to keep quiet. I thought I'd keep a low profile, pretend there was nothing wrong, but all the time be on the lookout, watching for clues. I had already discovered that there were four of them altogether and now I had to find out what kind of aliens they were and why they had come to Planet Earth.

Actually the answer to that question was pretty obvious. Aliens only come to Earth for one reason, and that is to take it over, to invade every bit of it. Everyone knows that. I mean, they're not likely to drive halfway across the universe just to ask if they can borrow some sugar.

By this time you will probably have worked out for yourself that I hadn't taken my last breath and died, otherwise I wouldn't be able to write this down for you. Evidently the aliens were not going to use a deadly virus. They had some other plan up their sleeve . . . assuming aliens have sleeves. If they don't, then what can they hide things up? Their nostrils? Armpits? Ears? I seem to be going off-track here a bit.

You can imagine my surprise, and my rampaging feelings, when Mum made the following announcement, shortly after lunch. "I've met the new neighbours," she said. "They seem nice. I've asked them over for a cup of coffee this afternoon, so we can meet the family."

The aliens are coming to our house – for tea and biscuits!

From *I'm Telling You They're Aliens*
Jeremy Strong

1. This story is written in (ring **one**):

the first person the third person.

1 mark

2. At what point does the narrator stop using the present tense ('talking' to the reader) and begin using the past tense (saying what happened)? Quote the first **five** words in your answer.

___

1 mark

3. A rhetorical question is a question where the speaker does not expect an answer. Give **one** example of a rhetorical question from this story.

___

1 mark

4. The word 'invade' means

___.

1 mark

5. If aliens would not come 'halfway across the universe just to ask if they can borrow some sugar', who do you think might make such a request and where would they come from?

___

2 marks

6. To have a plan 'up your sleeve' does not normally mean up a real sleeve. It means (ring **one**):

all ready to put into action to warm them up written down.

1 mark

7. The word 'rampaging' means (ring **one**):

uncomfortable wild thoughtful embarrassed.

1 mark

8. The phrase 'going off track' means (ring **one**):

digesting digressing diluting.

1 mark

9. What do you think will happen after this text, when the new neighbours come for tea?

1 mark

___

___

page 11
total out of 10

Octocure

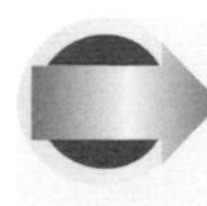

This poem uses nonsense words to describe an imaginary octopus, Oliver, and a nasty illness that he catches. The author, Alison Chisholm, has written many poems for both adults and children. She has also written books about how to write poetry.

Oliver the Octopus
Was feeling rather ill.
He went to see the doctopus
Who sent him for a pill.
He said, "That's chickenpoctopus,
Your tentacles are spotty."
Poor Olly got a shocktopus –
He felt a little dotty.
He bought four pairs of socktopus
To hide his spotty legs,
And fed himself on choctopus
And jellyfishes' eggs.
In just a week the octopus
Felt better than before.
The spots had gone – the doctopus
Had found the perfect cure.

Alison Chisholm

1. Which **two** of the following words best describe this poem?

funny   true   rhyming   limerick   serious   2 marks

2. Which real word can you find in **both** 'doctopus' **and** 'choctopus'?

____ 1 mark

3. Which made-up word reminds you of 'chicken pox'?

____ 1 mark

4. Which symptom of this illness does the octopus have?

____ 1 mark

5. Which **two** real words does the word 'doctopus' remind you of?

____

____ 2 marks

6. What food does the word 'choctopus' remind you of?

____ 1 mark

7. The name 'Oliver' is sometimes shortened. What is it shortened to in this poem?

____ 1 mark

8. Imagine that Oliver the octopus heard a knock at the door. Make up a funny word for the knock, and make sure that it rhymes with 'octopus'.

____ 1 mark

page 13
total out of 10

Odd girls

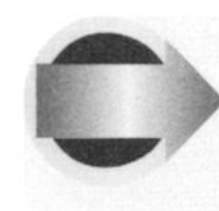

This is a rhyming poem written by John Coldwell – a teacher who also writes poems and stories for children.

There are some odd girls in our class
Like Sue whose head is made of glass.
She hangs around with Mary Minns
Whose head is built from baked bean tins.
Now, her best friend is Joanne Green
Whose head is made from plasticine.
And next to her sits Zara Good
Whose head is made from polished wood.
On the desk behind is Cathy Daw
Whose head's a bin bag stuffed with straw.
She is pals with Lucy Moon
And her head is a blue balloon.
At the back sits Tracey Dock
Whose head is just a lump of rock.

They think that I am strange
And leave me all alone.
Is it just because my head
Is made of flesh and bone?

John Coldwell

1 Read these statements.
Each is either 'True' (T), 'False' (F) or 'We cannot be sure' (?).
Put a tick in the correct box.

Tick one box only for each statement	T	F	?
a) Mary and Sue are good friends.			
b) Zara Good's head is made of oak.			
c) Sue's head is more fragile than Tracey's.			
d) Joanne is best friends with Zara.			
e) Lucy's head is green.			
f) The poem's narrator is a girl.			

6 marks

2 If the class register is arranged alphabetically, by surname, will Joanne come **before** or **after** Zara?

____

1 mark

3 Who has a metal head?

____

1 mark

4 Who sits in front of Cathy Daw?

____

1 mark

5 Which word does the poet use that means 'friends'?

____

1 mark

6 Whose surname do we not know?

____

1 mark

7 Why did the poet choose to make Zara's surname 'Good' and Tracey's surname 'Dock'?

____

____

1 mark

page 15
total out of 12

Teeth

This information text tells you about the different kinds of teeth that humans have at different stages of life.

Human beings have two sets of teeth in their lifetime – the primary dentition and the secondary dentition.

The Baby Teeth

The first set of 20 teeth are known as the baby, primary, deciduous or 'milk' teeth. They are called deciduous because they fall out (like leaves on a deciduous tree) to make room for the permanent teeth.

The milk teeth start to show through the gums when you are about six months old and start to fall out when you are about six years old.

The Adult Teeth

The second set of 32 teeth are known as the permanent or adult teeth. They are called permanent because, if you look after them properly, they stay with you permanently throughout your life.

The permanent teeth start to emerge when you are about six years old and have generally all emerged, apart from the wisdom teeth, by the age of about 12. Wisdom teeth appear between the ages of 17–21, although not everyone gets them.

Incisors

The incisors are the shovel-shaped teeth at the front of the mouth.

They are used for biting and cutting food.

Canines

The canine teeth – also known as 'eye teeth' – are more pointed and are found next to the incisors.

Canines are used for tearing and ripping food.

Premolars and Molars

The premolars and molars are also known as 'cheek teeth'. They have a large flat surface, are bigger and stronger than the front teeth and have more than one root. Young children don't have premolars, they just have molars behind the canines.

Premolars and molars are used for chewing, crushing and grinding the food.

Abridged from 'Different kinds of teeth'
Children's University website, University of Manchester

1. Which teeth are suited to taking a bite from an apple?

____ 1 mark

2. Do all adults have wisdom teeth?

____ 1 mark

3. How many teeth did you have when you were three years old?

____ 1 mark

4. Complete this sentence:
'Primary dentition' is to 'baby teeth' as 'secondary dentition' is to

____ . 1 mark

5. Give **two** other names for baby teeth or primary teeth.

____

____ 2 marks

6. Which teeth are pointed?

____ 1 mark

7. How does the layout of the text make it easy to pick out the names of the different kinds of teeth?

____

____ 1 mark

8. Ring the **two** words that best describe this text.

glossary information index flyer non-fiction 2 marks

page 17
total out of 10

Pelican

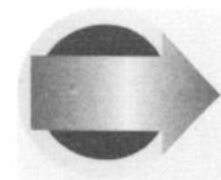

A pelican is a large bird that usually lives in hot countries. It has webbed feet and a long straight beak. From this beak hangs a big stretchy pouch of skin that it uses for catching and holding fish. Celia Warren, the author of this poem, has written many poems for children.

Pelican, Pelican,
Why so big a beak?
Is that where the words live
That you would like to speak?
Long words, special words,
Words to keep for best,
Words you've loved forever
Since your egg-days in the nest?

Pelican, Pelican,
I have words like that,
Safe inside my word-cage
Underneath my hat:
Dodecahedron,
Sycamore, rose,
Paprika, chameleon,
Words such as those.

Pelican, Pelican,
Open up your beak,
Share your thesaurus,
I long to hear you speak.
Ungainly and cumbersome,
You're not a pretty bird,
But, Pelican, your name is
My favourite feathered word.

Celia Warren

1. Who is the poet talking to in this poem?

____ 1 mark

2. Why do you think the poet repeats 'words' five times in the first verse?

____

____ 1 mark

3. What does the speaker mean by 'my word-cage'?

____ 1 mark

4. The poet chose the words 'dodecahedron', 'sycamore', 'rose', 'paprika' and 'chameleon' because (ring **one**):

they were hard to spell | she liked the sound of them

they reminded her of pelicans | they describe different kinds of birds. 1 mark

5. Write a definition for each of these favourite words on the line next to it. Use a dictionary to help you.

dodecahedron: ______________________________

sycamore: ______________________________

rose: ______________________________

paprika: ______________________________

chameleon: ______________________________ 5 marks

6. Give **two** reasons why a poem about a sparrow would have worked less well than this poem about a pelican.

____

____ 2 marks

7. Tomasz said he thought the poem was mainly about birds. Molly said she thought it was mainly about words. Who do you agree with and why?

____

____ 1 mark

page 19
total out of 12

Jorvik Viking Centre, Coppergate

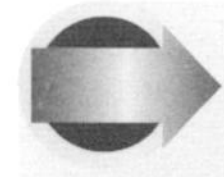

This text is taken from a guidebook about York, which is a very old city in the north of England. The guidebook was specially written for children and young people. There are some difficult words in this text, so a glossary is provided. The name 'Jorvik' is the Viking name for York and is pronounced 'Yorvik'.

This world famous centre is built on the site of an archaeological dig that was started in 1976. A complete Viking village has been recreated, with houses, workshops and a **quayside**. The 'time cars' take you back to Viking times and you can see, hear and smell what life might have been like in Jorvik in the tenth century.

An exhibition shows how it has been possible to recreate the faces of the Viking inhabitants of Jorvik. Using a skull found in 1986, realistic 3-D models have been produced using computer technology. Gradually the Viking figures on display are being replaced by these models. There is also an exhibition of treasures found during the **excavations**: combs, belt buckles and jewellery.

As you leave the Centre, don't miss the chance to see a coin being made, as it was in Viking times. A round piece of **pewter** is placed between two dies and a sharp blow with a hammer makes impressions on both sides of the coin. Jorvik's city mint made silver pennies and it was second only to London in its importance as a coin-producing centre.

The Jorvik Centre is a very popular attraction in York. To avoid queuing it is best to visit first thing in the morning, although buskers do provide entertainment while you are waiting during the day.

Open: Apr–Oct, daily 9am–7pm. Nov–March, daily 9am–5.30pm.

Closed: Christmas Day.

Tel: (01904) 643211.

Check that these details are up to date before visiting.

From *Pathways to Literacy: City of York*
Gill Matthews

Glossary

excavations large-scale digging causing holes
pewter a metal that is a mixture of tin and lead or some other metal
quayside an area usually made of stone or iron, where boats are landed and launched, or loaded and unloaded

1. The adjective 'archaeological' relates to which noun? (ring **one**)

architecture archaeology archangel

1 mark

2. What does 'archaeological' mean? (ring **one**)

relating to the study of relics digging up land

a Viking settlement a collection of old papers

1 mark

3. Coppergate is an area of which city?

____

1 mark

4. Which senses will a trip in a 'time car' appeal to? (ring any that apply)

touch smell sound taste sight

3 marks

5. If you have to queue to get into the museum, who will entertain you while you are waiting? (ring **one**)

clowns street musicians chimpanzees Vikings

1 mark

6. Where was the most important coin-producing centre in Britain in Viking times?

____

1 mark

7. Emma and Dan visited the Jorvik Centre last June. They stayed until the Centre closed. What time did they leave?

____

1 mark

8. Name **two** treasures that Emma and Dan might have seen in the exhibition.

____

____

2 marks

9. Why is some of the text put inside a box?

____

____

1 mark

page 21
total out of 12

City sounds heard after dark

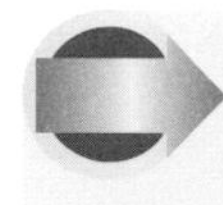

This poem is by Wes Magee, who was once a teacher but then became a full-time writer. Many of his poems and stories are good for reading aloud and acting out. He has also written some plays.

The sweesh sweesh of speeding cars.
Old songs from the crowded bars.
Disco drums and loud guitars.

Aircraft zapping through the sky.
Rooftop cats that spit and cry.
Laughter from the passers-by.

Motorbikers' sudden roar.
Corner lads who josh and jaw.
A call. A shout. A slammed door.

The guard dogs that howl and bark.
Voices from the padlocked park.
City sounds heard after dark.

Wes Magee

1. Describe the rhyme pattern.

1 mark

2. Which made-up word sounds like a mixture of 'sweep' and 'swish'?

1 mark

3. The poet uses repetition in the first line. What effect does this have?

1 mark

4. What style of music is being played and where are the 'bars', do you think?

2 marks

5. Reread the third verse, which contains the line, 'Corner lads who **josh** and **jaw**'. Write the meaning of each word on the line next to it.

'josh':

'jaw':

2 marks

6. What might we guess is happening from the line, 'Voices from the padlocked park'?

1 mark

7. Reading the poem, Joe made up this extra line for one verse:
'Pigeons cooing as they fly.'
To which verse did Joe add his new line? Why did he choose this verse?

2 marks

8. Make up a new line for one of the other verses. Explain how and why you chose your words. (Think about meaning, rhythm and rhyme.)

2 marks

page 23
total out of 12

On the Yellow Brick Road

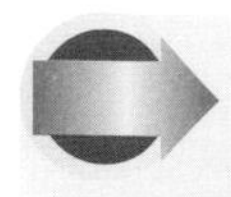

This playscript is based on *The Wizard of Oz* by L. Frank Baum, which was first published at the beginning of the twentieth century. Here we meet some of the main characters. L. Frank Baum was an American writer who wrote many other children's stories.

Setting: A yellow road leading through the forest towards the Emerald City.

Enter, stage left, Dorothy (carrying dog), Tin Man (carrying oil can) and Scarecrow, who trips and falls.

Tin Man (*pulling Scarecrow to his feet*): Why didn't you walk around that hole?
Scarecrow: I don't know enough. (*cheerfully*) My head is stuffed with straw. That's why I'm going to the great Oz – to ask him for some brains.
Dorothy (*putting Toto down*): How long will it be before we are out of the forest?
Tin Man: I have never been to the Emerald City, so I don't know. But my father went there once. He said it was a long and dangerous journey – but nearer the City, where Oz lives, the country is beautiful.
Dorothy: Aren't you frightened?
Tin Man: No. I am not afraid as long as I have my oil can. (*giving his neck a squirt of oil*)

Enter Lion, who rushes towards Dorothy and snaps at Toto. Dorothy picks up dog and holds him close.

Dorothy: Don't you dare bite Toto! (*tapping Lion's nose*) You ought to be ashamed of yourself, a big beast like you, trying to bite a little dog! You are a big coward.
Lion (*hanging his head*): Yes, I am. (*gently patting Toto*) It's true, your dog is very small. (*sadly*) Only a coward like me would think of biting him.
Scarecrow (*to Lion*): The King of Beasts shouldn't be a coward!
Lion (*tearfully wiping eye with his tail*): I know. It is my great sorrow. But whenever there is danger I am afraid. My heart beats so fast that I fear it might burst!
Scarecrow: Well, why don't you ask Oz for courage? I'm going to ask him for some brains.
Tin Man: And I am going to ask him for a heart.
Dorothy: And I am going to ask him to send Toto and me back home to Kansas. You'd be very welcome to join us.
Lion: Then I will, because my life is unbearable without courage.

All exit, stage right.

Adapted from *The Wizard of Oz*
L. Frank Baum (1856–1919)

1. Some words appear inside brackets.

   a) What are they for?

   ____________________ 1 mark

   b) Why are they in italics?

   ____________________ 1 mark

   c) Why are the words 'a' and 'the' missed out?

   ____________________ 1 mark

2. How many players would you need to act out this scene?

   ____________________ 1 mark

3. What place does the Yellow Brick Road lead to?

   ____________________ 1 mark

4. What is the Tin Man hoping to receive when he arrives there?

   ____________________ 1 mark

5. What does the Lion say happens to him whenever he faces danger?

   ____________________ 1 mark

6. Who do these four characters hope will help them?

   ____________________ 1 mark

7. Imagine that you and your friends are staging this scene. Write some notes describing the stage plan. Your notes should include, for example, what you would paint on the scenery and what 'props' your actors would need.

   ____

   ____

   ____

   ____________________ 2 marks

page 25
total out of 10

House on fire!

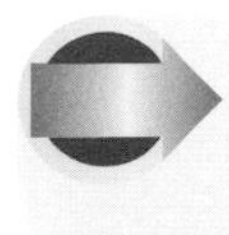

This text is from a long poem called *A Child's Christmas in Wales* by Dylan Thomas. Dylan Thomas was Welsh and the poem is also available in the Welsh language.

Something was burning all right;
Perhaps it was Mr Prothero, who always slept
there after midday dinner with a newspaper
over his face. But he was standing in the middle
of the room, saying, "A fine Christmas!"
and smacking at the smoke with a slipper.
"Call the fire brigade," cried Mrs Prothero
as she beat the gong.

"They won't be there," said Mr Prothero,
"it's Christmas."

There was no fire to be seen, only clouds of smoke
and Mr Prothero standing in the middle of them,
waving his slipper as though he were conducting.

"Do something," he said.

And we threw all our snowballs into the smoke –
I think we missed Mr Prothero – and ran out
of the house to the telephone box.

"Let's call the police as well," Jim said.

"And the ambulance."

"And Ernie Jenkins, he likes fires."

But we only called the fire brigade, and soon
the fire engine came and three tall men in helmets
brought a hose into the house and Mr Prothero
got out just in time before they turned it on.
Nobody could have had a noisier Christmas Eve.
And when the firemen turned off the hose and
were standing in the wet smoky room, Jim's aunt,
Miss Prothero, came downstairs and peered in
at them. Jim and I waited, very quietly, to hear what
she would say to them. She said the right thing,
always. She looked at the three tall firemen in their
shining helmets, standing among the smoke and
cinders and dissolving snowballs, and she said:
"Would you like anything to read?"

From *A Child's Christmas in Wales*
Dylan Thomas (1914–1953)

1. Why does Mr Prothero think the fire brigade won't be available?

____ 1 mark

2. What does he mean by "A fine Christmas!"?

____

____ 1 mark

3. What indications are there that this is not a twenty-first century household?

____

____ 2 marks

4. The children considered making various phone calls. Which one was **not** to an emergency service?

____ 1 mark

5. Why do you think they called only the fire brigade in the end?

____ 1 mark

6. What might the firemen have expected Miss Prothero to be offering when she began, "Would you like anything to ..."?

____ 1 mark

7. a) Why was Mr Prothero smacking at the smoke with a slipper?

____

b) Do you think he was sensible to do this? Explain your answer.

____ 2 marks

8. Were the boys more excited by or afraid of the fire? Explain your answer.

____

____

____ 1 mark

page 27
total out of 10

The story of Helen Keller

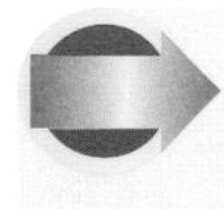

This text is a short biography of an American woman called Helen Keller. A biography is a non-fiction account about the life of a real person. It usually gives the dates of the person's birth and death. It also tells you about key events in the person's life.

Helen Keller was born on 27 June 1880 and for 18 months was a happy, healthy baby. Then, suddenly, she became ill and very nearly died. When she recovered, her parents realised that Helen had lost her eyesight and hearing: she was deaf and blind.

They continued to care for their little girl at home in Alabama, USA, but it was not easy. Helen clung to her mother's skirt, feeling lost. She recognised people by feeling their faces and clothing. She touched people's hands to discover what they were doing. When Helen wanted some bread, she made her parents understand by pretending to cut a loaf. For ice cream, she hugged herself and shivered. But this was not enough. She could not understand the world around her.

At last, when Helen was six, a teacher arrived who was to change her life. Anne Sullivan had once been blind herself. Slowly and patiently, she taught the little girl how to spell words with her fingers. Helen copied, but did not understand what she was doing.

One day, Anne led Helen to a water-pump. Holding her hand under the water, she signed W-A-T-E-R into Helen's hand. Suddenly, the little girl understood. The signs represented what was pouring over her hand. Excitedly, she led Anne everywhere, picking up familiar things – now a doll; now a cake: within an hour she had learnt 30 words.

Helen no longer felt shut out of the world. Later, Anne taught her to read in Braille, by feeling patterns of raised dots on a page. Helen grew up to go to college and write her autobiography. She became famous, travelling the world, giving lectures and helping other deaf and blind people to live full, happy lives. Helen died soon after her 88th birthday, in 1968.

1 'Deaf' is to 'hearing' as ______________________ is to 'eyesight'. — 1 mark

2 Read these statements.
After each one, write T for 'True' or F for 'False'.

a) Helen Keller was under two years old when she became ill. ______ — 1 mark

b) Helen's illness made her go deaf and blind. ______ — 1 mark

c) Helen's parents put her into a care home in Alabama. ______ — 1 mark

d) Helen licked her lips when she wanted an ice cream. ______ — 1 mark

e) The first word Helen understood in sign language was 'water'. ______ — 1 mark

3 Once Helen understood that the wetness she could feel on her hand had a name, 'water', how did it make her feel, and why?

____

____ — 2 marks

4 How did Helen recognise a person who was in a room with her?

____ — 1 mark

5 How did she find out what other people were doing?

____ — 1 mark

6 Blind people learning to read use lettering made up of raised dots on paper. What is the name of this lettering?

____ — 1 mark

7 Helen grew up to write a book. What was it about?

____ — 1 mark

page 29
total out of 12

Rebecca

who slammed doors for fun and perished miserably

This poem was first published in 1907. The author, Hilaire Belloc, wrote many other poems. Many of his poems tell a story that teaches us something – and they warn us of what may happen if we take no notice! There are some difficult words in this poem, so a glossary is provided.

A trick that everyone abhors
In little girls is slamming doors.
A wealthy banker's little daughter
Who lived in Palace Green, Bayswater
(By name Rebecca Offendort),
Was given to this furious sport.
She would deliberately go
And slam the door like Billy-Ho!
To make her Uncle Jacob start.
She was not really bad at heart,
But only rather rude and wild:
She was an **aggravating** child…

It happened that a **marble bust**
Of Abraham was standing just
Above the door this little lamb
Had carefully prepared to slam,
And down it came! It knocked her flat!
It laid her out! She looked like that.

Her funeral **sermon** (which was long
And followed by a **sacred** song)
Mentioned her virtues, it is true,
But dwelt upon her vices too,
And showed the dreadful end of one
Who goes and slams the door for fun.

The children who were brought to hear
The awful tale from far and near
Were much impressed, and inly swore
They never more would slam the door.
– As often they had done before.

Hilaire Belloc (1870–1953)

Glossary

aggravating annoying, troublesome
marble bust a sculpture in stone, showing the top half of someone's body
sacred holy, set aside for God
sermon a formal talk aiming to encourage good behaviour

1. Which words in the poem or its title mean 'died in unhappy circumstances'?

____ 1 mark

2. What does 'abhor' mean? (ring **one**)

avoid   practise   find   dislike   favour   1 mark

3. If a virtue is good behaviour, what is a vice?

____ 1 mark

4. What was Rebecca's father's job?

____ 1 mark

5. What was it that made the statue fall?

____ 1 mark

6. Which words suggest that the poem originally had an illustration to go with it?

____ 1 mark

7. The word 'start' often means 'begin'. What different meaning does it have here (verse 1, line 9)?

____ 1 mark

8. How do we know that Rebecca was not the only child to slam doors?

____

____ 1 mark

9. What do you think is the purpose of the last verse?

____

____ 1 mark

10. Which word means 'inwardly'?

____ 1 mark

page 31
total out of 10

Steam train stories

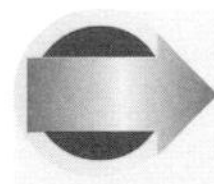

This text is taken from *The Railway Children*, which was first published in 1906. The author, E. Nesbit, wrote many other children's books, including *Five Children and It* and *The Phoenix and the Carpet*. In this text the main characters in the story meet the local station porter, who tells them all about life on the railway. Trains were then powered by steam (made using fire and water) and not by electricity or diesel as they are today.

When their father is suddenly taken away, Roberta, Peter and Phyllis go with their mother to live in a country cottage in Yorkshire – where they have all kinds of adventures.

They reached the station and spent a joyous two hours with the Porter. He was a worthy man and seemed never tired of answering the questions that began with "Why –" which many people in higher ranks of life often seem weary of.

He told them many things that they had not known before – as, for instance, that the things that hook carriages together are called couplings, and that the pipes like great serpents that hang over the couplings are meant to stop the train with.

"If you could get a holt of one o' them when the train is going and pull 'em apart," said he, "she'd stop dead off with a jerk."

"Who's she?" said Phyllis.

"The train, of course," said the Porter. After that the train was never again 'It' to the children.

"And you know the thing in the carriages where it says on it, 'Five pounds' fine for improper use.' If you was to improperly use that, the train 'ud stop."

"And if you used it properly?" said Roberta.

"It 'ud stop just the same, I suppose," said he, "but it isn't proper use unless you're being murdered. There was an old lady once – someone kidded her on it was a refreshment-room bell, and she used it improper, not being in danger of her life, though hungry, and when the train stopped and the guard came along expecting to find someone weltering in their last moments, she says, 'Oh, please, Mister, I'll take a glass of stout and a Bath bun,' she says. And the train was seven minutes behind time as it was."

"What did the guard say to the old lady?"

"*I* dunno," replied the Porter, "but I lay she didn't forget it in a hurry, whatever it was."

From *The Railway Children*
E. Nesbit (1858–1924)

1. What are Peter's sisters called?

____ 2 marks

2. The word 'weary' means

____. 1 mark

3. What features of this text suggest that it is fiction?

____

____ 2 marks

4. What are 'couplings'?

____ 1 mark

5. What was the penalty for pressing the bell to stop the train when there was no emergency?

____ 1 mark

6. The author has spelt some words differently from usual. This is to show how the Porter speaks with a Yorkshire accent. Explain what the Porter means when he uses these words (underlined).

   a) "If you could get a <u>holt</u> of one <u>o'</u> them when the train is going and pull 'em apart," said he, "she'd stop dead off with a jerk."

   ____ 2 marks

   b) "... the train <u>'ud</u> stop."

   ____ 1 mark

7. The Porter uses many old-fashioned words, such as 'weltering' (rolling around), and some slang. In your own words, explain what he means by the following.

   a) 'someone kidded her on'

   ____ 1 mark

   b) 'I lay she didn't forget it in a hurry'

   ____ 1 mark

page 33
total out of 12

A great storm in Scotland

This text is taken from the beginning of the novel *The Water Horse* by Dick King-Smith, first published in 1990. Read the text to see how the story starts. Read the whole book to find out what happens the morning after the great storm, when Kirstie and her brother Angus find something very strange on the beach.

In the small hours of March the 26th, 1930, a great storm struck the west coast of Scotland. The huge seas that it had whipped up smashed against the foot of the cliffs, and the tigerish tempest ran up the face of them and grabbed a small white house on the cliff top in its jaws.

The house quivered and shook in the teeth of the wind, and Kirstie, waking in sudden fright, was sure that the roof must go.

The noise of the storm was fearful. Angus will be terrified, thought Kirstie, and she jumped out of bed and ran to her little brother's room next door. Her mother arrived at the same moment carrying an oil lamp, and by its light they could see that Angus was sleeping peacefully, sleeping like the baby he had been only a few years before. Outside, the thunder banged and the lightning flashed, the wind roared and the rain poured. Angus snored.

"Back to bed, Kirstie," said her mother. "I'll stay here awhile in case he wakes."

"What about Grumble?" said Kirstie. "Is he all right?"

Grumble was Mother's father, who lived with them. When Kirstie was very small, she had heard Mother say angrily to him one day, "All you ever do is grumble, grumble," and so she had thought that it was his name. It suited him. He came stumping along the corridor now, a big old man with a thick droopy moustache.

"Can't sleep a wink!" growled Grumble to his daughter and granddaughter, as though it was their fault. "Terrible weather! The Lord help sailors on a night like this!"

From *The Water Horse*
Dick King-Smith

1. The hours after midnight, when the times of day are in small numbers (such as one, two or three o'clock), are sometimes called the _______________ hours.

   1 mark

2. The tempest is described as 'tigerish'. In what other way does the description of the storm remind you of an animal?

   ____

   1 mark

3. Where is Kirstie's house?

   ____

   1 mark

4. Kirstie fears that 'the roof must go'. What does she mean by this?

   ____

   1 mark

5. Is Angus older or younger than his sister?

   ____

   1 mark

6. What is Angus doing that shows he is asleep?

   ____

   1 mark

7. If 'Grumble' really was Grandfather's name, what change would you make to the sentence "All you ever do is grumble, grumble"?

   ____

   1 mark

8. Who is Grumble worried about when the storm wakes him?

   ____

   1 mark

9. What tells you that the house has no electricity?

   ____

   1 mark

10. What words does Grumble use to tell Kirstie and her mother that the storm is disturbing his sleep?

    ____

    1 mark

page 35
total out of 10

Tom finds happiness

This text is taken from the children's classic *The Water Babies*, which was first published in 1863. At that time, many poor children, like Tom in this story, did not go to school but had to work instead. Often the work was very hard and they were paid very little money.

Ten-year-old Tom, a chimney sweep, has run away. At last, he finds himself in a river. His grown-up pursuers think him drowned, but they are wrong. He is now a water baby ...

Tom was now amphibious; and what is better still, he was clean. For the first time in his life, he felt how comfortable it was to have nothing on him but himself. But he only enjoyed it: he did not know it, or think about it.

He did not remember having ever been dirty. Indeed, he did not remember any of his old troubles – being tired, or hungry, or beaten, or sent up dark chimneys. Since that sweet sleep, he had forgotten all about his master, and Harthover Place, and the little white girl and, in a word, all that had happened to him when he lived before; and what was best of all, he had forgotten all the bad words which he had learned from Grimes and the rude boys who had once been his playmates.

Tom was very happy in the water. He had been sadly overworked in the land-world; and so now, to make up for that, he had nothing but holidays in the water-world for a long, long time to come. He had nothing to do now but enjoy himself, and look at all the pretty things which are to be seen in the cool clear water-world, where the sun is never too hot, and the frost is never too cold.

Abridged from *The Water Babies*
Charles Kingsley (1819–1875)

…uction to this text is in a paragraph of its own. What else do you notice

…he text in the introduction is set out?

____ 1 mark

… the tense of each verb in the introduction and how this differs from the verb tenses used in the text?

____ 2 marks

2 The word 'amphibious' is (ring **one**):

a verb   a noun   an adjective   an adverb.   1 mark

3 In what **two** kinds of habitat can an amphibious creature live?

____

____ 2 marks

4 What was Tom's job before he became a water baby?

____ 1 mark

5 Name **two** of Tom's 'troubles' in the 'land-world' that he has left.

____

____ 2 marks

6 'Playmates' is an old-fashioned word. What word might we now use instead?

____ 1 mark

7 How hot or cold is it in Tom's watery world?

____ 1 mark

8 Give **one** word that describes Tom's mood in the water.

____ 1 mark

page 37
total out of 12

The milkmaid and her pail

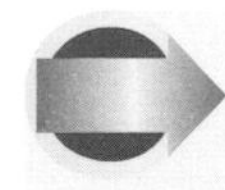

This tale was first told by Aesop (pronounced 'eesop'), a Greek slave who liv[...] over 2500 years ago and made up hundreds of stories. People passed on thes[...] stories to their children and grandchildren, but they were not written down unti[...] the nineteenth century.

There was once a poor farmer who had a daughter. This daughter was always day-dreaming.

"Your head is in the clouds," scolded the farmer. "It is time you learned to milk the cows."

The farmer's daughter did not want to be a milkmaid. Instead, she wanted to become rich. When she had finished milking the cows, she put the pail of milk on her head and set off to the dairy, musing to herself as she walked.

"The milk in this pail will provide me with cream," she reasoned, "and from the cream I shall make butter. Then I shall sell the butter. With the money from the sale of the butter, I shall buy eggs. When the eggs hatch, they will produce chickens. My chickens will lay more eggs. Before long I shall have a whole yard full of poultry. Then I shall sell some hens. With the money I shall buy a fine silk gown."

The milkmaid spun around, swirling her imaginary skirt.

"All the young men will admire my gown," the milkmaid told herself. "But when they come a-courting," she added proudly, "I shall toss my head and have nothing to do with them."

With these words, the milkmaid tossed her head. Down went the pail. All the milk was spilled, and all the milkmaid's dreams were broken.

Moral: do not count your chickens before they are hatched.